Start Up Science

GODFREY HALL 2

Illustrated by Beverley Sprio

©1997 Times Media Private Limited
© 2003 Marshall Cavendish International (Singapore) Private Limited

Published by Marshall Cavendish Education
An imprint of Marshall Cavendish International (Singapore) Private Limited
A member of Times Publishing Limited
Times Centre, 1 New Industrial Road, Singapore 536196
Customer Service Hotline: (65) 6213 9106
E-mail: fps@sg.marshallcavendish.com
Website: www.marshallcavendish.com/education/sg

First published 1997
Reprinted 1998, 2000, 2001, 2002, 2003, 2004 (twice), 2005

ISBN 981-01-0661-0

Printed in Singapore by Stamford Press Pte Ltd

CONTENTS

1. Is It Magnetic?

Some things are attracted by a magnet. They are pulled towards it. We call them **magnetic** materials. Magnets are used as parts for the making of things like loudspeakers and can be found in some door catches. The first magnets were made over 2,000 years ago.

Tick the things below that you think are magnetic, then test them out using a magnet.

Object	I think it is magnetic	I know it is magnetic
marble		
pencil		
paper clip		
coin		
metal spoon		

2. MAKING A MAGNET

It is easy to make your own magnet. You can then use it to pick up magnetic materials. It is important to know that a magnet can be weakened by dropping or knocking it so be careful when you move it.

You will need

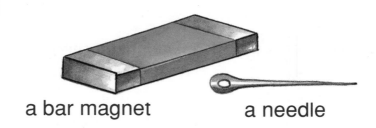

a bar magnet   a needle

1. Stroke your magnet along the needle one way. Do this about 50 times.Stroke it in one direction.

2. Make sure you hold the needle away from the magnet after each stroke.

Your needle has now become a magnet. Test it out and see if you can do the following things with your new magnet:

1. How many pins can you pick up with it?

_____

2. Make another magnet using the bar magnet. Does it make a difference if you only stroke it 40 times?

_____

3. What happens when you put the ends of your two magnets together?

_____

3. How Strong Is Your Magnet?

Once you have made your own magnet, you will want to test it to see how strong it is. The stronger the magnet, the more it will pick up.

There are a number of tests you can make to see how strong your magnet is. Collect together some paper clips. How many paper clips will your magnet hold?

Which is the strongest end?

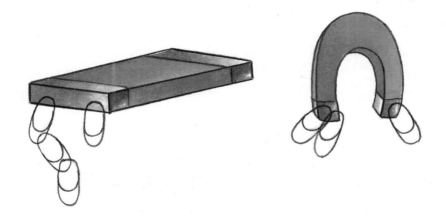

Look at these pictures. Number them 1, 2, 3, 4 beginning with the strongest magnet.

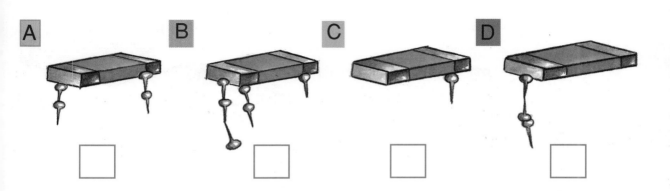

4. NORTH AND SOUTH POLE

Magnets have two ends, the North Pole and the South Pole. If a magnet is hung from a piece of cord, it will always swing round and come to rest in the same position. The Earth is in fact a huge magnet.

Try this.

Hang two bar magnets from cords. Bring the two ends together. If they **repel** or push away from each other, they are both North or both South. If they **attract** or pull towards each other, one will be North and the other South.

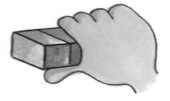

Tape a bar magnet on the top of a toy car. See if you can pull your car along using another magnet.

See if the magnets in these drawings below attract or repel.

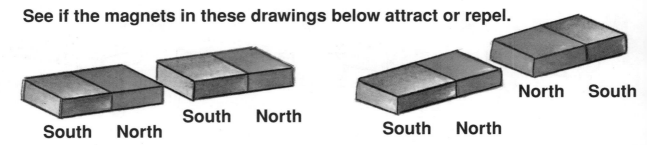

South   North   South   North

South   North   North   South

 A

The two magnets will

_____.

 B

The two magnets will

_____.

6

5. Making A Magnet Game

There are lots of different games you can make using magnets. You can cut out some animal shapes and stick paper clips onto them. Then hang a magnet from a string and use it 'to catch' the animals.

Here is a simple maze game you can make.

You will need:

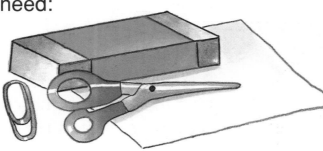

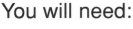

scissors
a piece of card
a paper clip
a bar magnet

1. Cut out a piece of card 20 centimetres square.

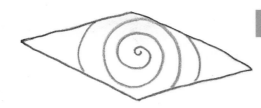

2. Draw a maze on one side of the card.

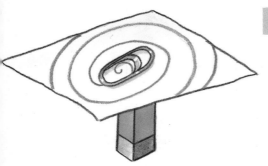

3. Put the paper clip at the start of the maze and take it to the middle pulling it along from underneath the card using the bar magnet.

See which of your friends can get the clip to the middle of the maze in the shortest time.

6. USES AT HOME

Some things we use at home work with the help of magnets. They can be used to keep cupboards shut and notes on fridges.

Look at this picture. Can you see any magnets? Circle them.

See if you can complete the sentences with the helping words given.

1. A magnet has a _____ Pole and a South Pole.
   (North / East)

2. The North Pole and the South Pole of magnets will _____. (attract / repel)

3. A steel pen and a paper _____ can be attracted by a magnet. (clip / boat)

4. Put two North ends of two magnets together and they will _____. (attract / repel)

5. Magnets can _____ or pull other magnets. (push / spill)

6. You can make a magnet out of a _____.
   (plastic comb / needle)

We use a **compass** to find our way. The needle of a **compass** always points North. Using a compass, we can see if we are going North, South, West or East. **Compasses** are used on ships and planes.

This is a compass. Look at the position of the needle and the eight points on the compass.

Which direction would you be going if you were on your way to the:

1. _____

2. _____

3. _____

4. _____

5. _____

6. _____

8. MAKING YOUR OWN COMPASS

See if you can make your own compass by following these steps.

You will need:

a dish of water

a magnet

a needle

a piece of cork

1. Take your needle. Stroke it in one direction 40 times with the magnet. Do not bang it.

2. Cut a slice of cork. Lay the needle carefully in the cork.

3. Place the cork onto the water in the dish.

4. The needle should point North. Check this using a compass.

9. ELECTROMAGNETS

Do you know that magnets are used in machines like cranes? These magnets are called **electromagnets**. **Electromagnets** are used to sort out scrap iron from other materials. They will only work when the power is switched on. The crane lowers the magnet. The power is switched on and it picks up just the things that are attracted to the magnet.

Look at how the crane works. Colour the things which you think the crane can pick up.

10. ELECTRICITY AT HOME

We need electricity to use some of the things we have at home.

Look at the drawing below. Colour the things that work by electricity.

What else in your house is worked by electricity?

Things in my house that work by electricity:

1. _____

2. _____

3. _____

4. _____

5. _____

11. DANGERS OF ELECTRICITY

Electricity can be used to help us. It can also be dangerous. If too many things are plugged on at the same time or if wires are not covered, we could get hurt. We must always take care.

Look at the picture. Use a red pen to circle any dangers that you can see.

Electricity needs to be able to 'flow' along a pathway. This is called a **circuit**. If there is a break in the **circuit**, the electricity cannot flow. A **circuit** must be joined together to work.

Here is one way to make a simple circuit.

You will need:

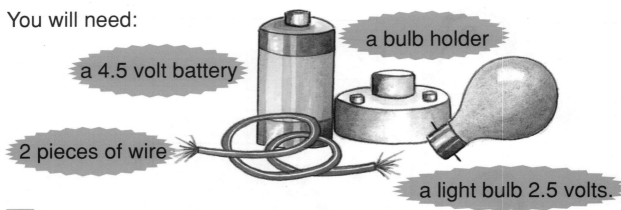

a bulb holder

a 4.5 volt battery

2 pieces of wire

a light bulb 2.5 volts.

1. Fix the bulb into the bulb holder.

2. Fix a wire to one end of the bulb holder and one end to the + end of the battery.

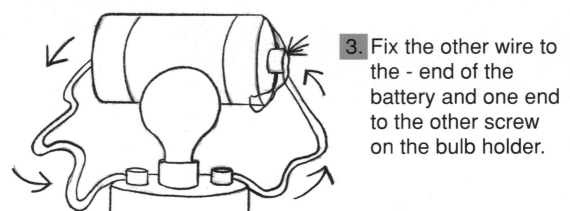

3. Fix the other wire to the - end of the battery and one end to the other screw on the bulb holder.

This drawing shows a complete circuit. The arrows show how the electricity flows. Now colour the drawing.

13. Inside A Battery

Look at the inside of this battery. The carbon rod and chemical paste help the battery to work properly. You should **never** take a battery to pieces. The chemical paste is very dangerous.

Unscramble the names of the different parts.

rbcaon dor ✎ hcemlica stpae ✎ seca

B. _____

A. _____

C. _____

Finish these sentences.

1. Never take a _____ to pieces. (magnet / battery)

2. The chemicals inside a battery are _____ .
   (dangerous / colourful)

3. Batteries are used in _____ . (torches / sandwiches)

4. Toys are sometimes _____ by batteries. (eaten / run)

5. As the chemicals are used up the battery gets _____ .
   (stronger / weaker)

Some materials allow electricity to flow through them. Others do not. The ones that electricity passes through are called **conductors**. Metal is a good **conductor** of electricity.

Which of these things is a good conductor of electricity? You can test them using a circuit.

		Good conductors
1.	metal spoon	yes / no
2.	wooden ruler	yes / no
3.	paper clip	yes / no
4.	plastic pen top	yes / no
5.	rubber	yes / no

If the bulb lights up, the material is a conductor of electricity.

You have learnt that electricity flows round a circuit. It will only flow if there is no break in the circuit.

Which of these circuits will sound the buzzer? Colour the buzzers that will sound.

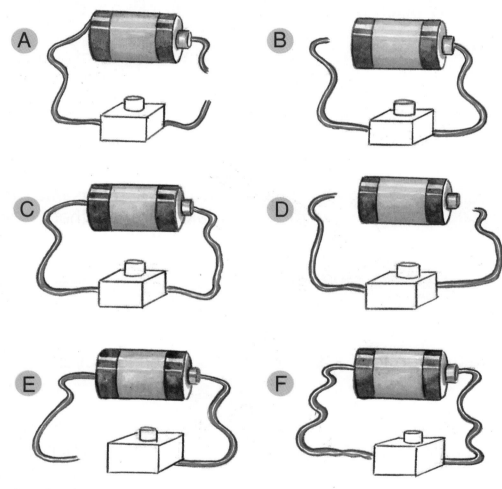

A

B

C

D

E

F

Draw a circuit of your own.

A **switch** can be used to turn a light on and off. When it is off, the circuit is broken. The light goes off. When it is on, the electricity can flow round and the light can go on.

You can make a switch of your own. You will need:

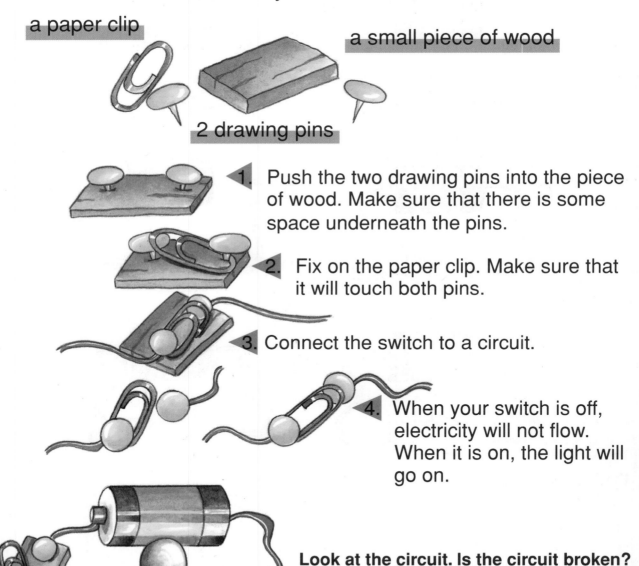

a paper clip

a small piece of wood

2 drawing pins

1. Push the two drawing pins into the piece of wood. Make sure that there is some space underneath the pins.

2. Fix on the paper clip. Make sure that it will touch both pins.

3. Connect the switch to a circuit.

4. When your switch is off, electricity will not flow. When it is on, the light will go on.

Look at the circuit. Is the circuit broken? Redraw the switch so that the bulb lights up.

17. MAKING LIGHT

We need light to see the things around us. Light is made in many different ways. The sun gives us light and so does fire. We can make our own light at night using a torch or the headlights of a car.

Put an 'N' by the natural lights and an 'M' by the man-made lights below.

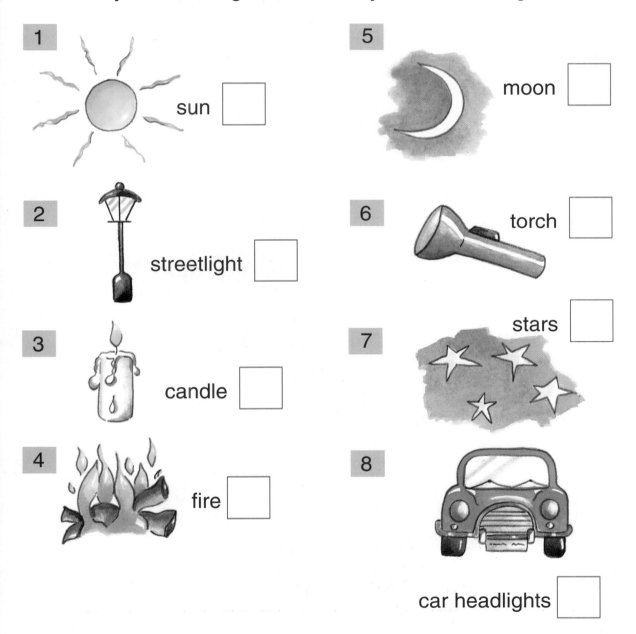

1   sun ☐

2   streetlight ☐

3   candle ☐

4   fire ☐

5   moon ☐

6   torch ☐

stars ☐

7

8   car headlights ☐

19

18. Light And Water

Light appears to bend when it enters water. That is why things appear different when they are placed in water. Place a pencil into a glass of water. When you look at it from above, it will look as if it is bent.

Water also makes things look bigger. It magnifies them.

Look at the cat in the picture. What can you see? Colour the part of the cat that looks bigger.

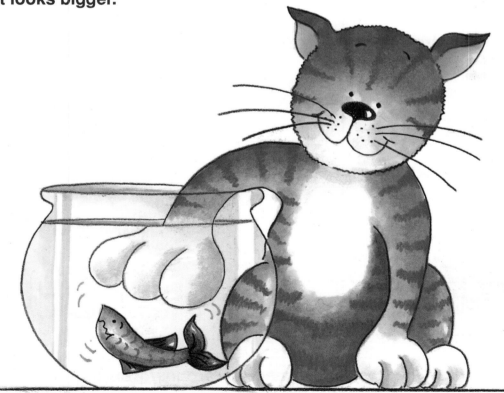

We can see through some materials like glass and some types of plastic. These materials are **transparent**. Other materials like wood and metal are **opaque**. We cannot see through them.

Tick the materials that are transparent. Put a cross by those that are opaque.

1. glass ☐

2. cardboard ☐

3. water ☐

4. clay ☐

5. metal ☐

6. wood ☐

7. clear plastic ☐

8. newspaper ☐

Make your own simple mask.

Trace the outline of the mask onto a piece of cardboard. Fix on some lenses using red or green clear plastic. What colours can you see through your mask? Try using lenses of different colours.

20. COLOURS

A rainbow is made of seven colours. They are red, orange, yellow, green, blue, indigo and violet. These are the colours of a **spectrum**. When these colours are all mixed together, they look white.

Try making a colour spinner.

1. Draw a circle onto a thin piece of card.

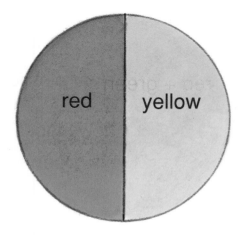

red   yellow

2. Divide the circle into half.

3. Colour in one side red and the other side yellow.

4. Push a pencil through the centre. When you spin the card, what colour can you see?

Try out some of these colour spinners. Spin the cards and see what colours you can get.

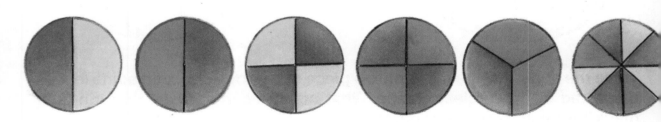

21. MIXING COLOURS

You can mix colours to make a new colour using paints, coloured pencils and felt tips. Red, blue and green are called primary colours.

What do you get if you mix these colours?

red + blue

red + green

blue + green + red

green + blue

You can try mixing other colours on your own.

23

22. MAKE YOUR OWN RAINBOW

You often see a rainbow after a shower or in the early morning or late at night. If you are in a plane and look down, you might see that a rainbow forms a complete circle. Remember a rainbow has no end. We often see a rainbow as an arch when we are on the ground because we are only seeing a part of it.

You can make your own rainbow by following these easy steps.

You will need:

water

a plastic dish

a mirror

white card

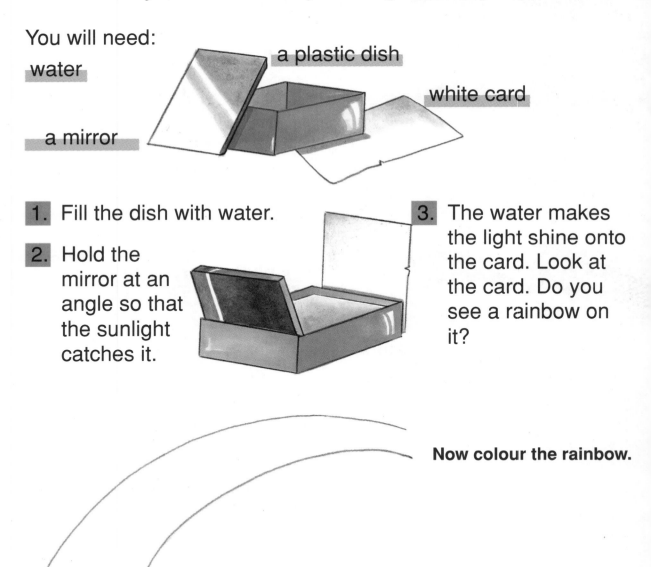

1. Fill the dish with water.

2. Hold the mirror at an angle so that the sunlight catches it.

3. The water makes the light shine onto the card. Look at the card. Do you see a rainbow on it?

Now colour the rainbow.

23. MIRRORS

Most mirrors are made from sheets of glass with a shiny silver surface behind them. When you look in a mirror you will see your **reflection**.

Here is a simple game you can play with two mirrors.

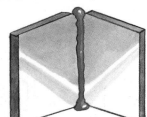

1. Put two mirrors together.

2. Put a small object between them.

3. Move the mirrors together and see how many reflections you can make.

Mirror writing can be used to send messages to a friend. It is also sometimes found on the front of ambulances and fire engines.

Put a mirror up against these words. What do the words say? Write them down in the blanks.

A HELLO _____

B GOOD DAY _____

C PRETTY POLLY _____

D HELP _____

E WELCOME _____

F STOP _____

Now, write out some secret sentences of your own.

1. _____

2. _____

3. _____

Shadows are made when light is blocked. Put your hand between a torch and the wall. The further your hand is from the light, the less light is blocked. That's why the further your hand is from the torch, the smaller the shadow gets.

Put your hand between a torch and the wall. See what different shapes you can make.

Go and stand in the sun for a few moments. Look at the ground. You should be able to see your own shadow.

Look at the pictures of the plants. Circle the letter of the picture where the shadow is shortest.

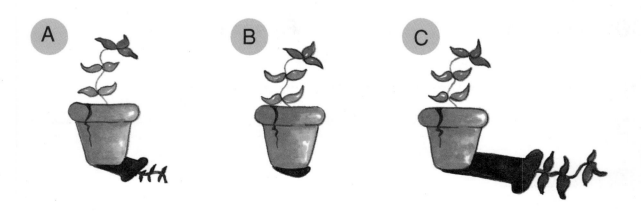

25. How Does It Move?

Things move in different ways. They can be blown by the wind, powered by a battery or pulled along by a horse or donkey. We can also move something by giving it a push.

Look at the words in the box. Which word helps to move each of the things in the pictures? Write the correct word in each blank.

wind ✎ engine ✎ pedals ✎ water

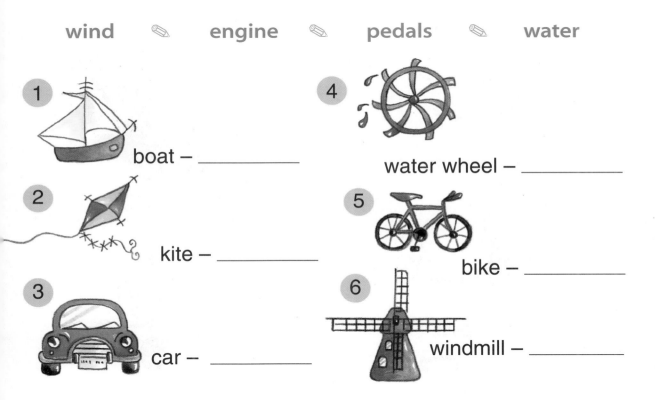

1 boat – _____

2 kite – _____

3 car – _____

4 water wheel – _____

5 bike – _____

6 windmill – _____

Tick the things that work by battery power.

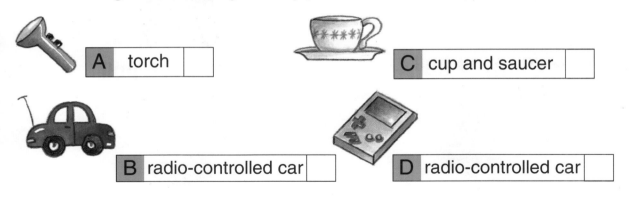

A torch

C cup and saucer

B radio-controlled car

D radio-controlled car

26. PUSH OR PULL

To get things moving, we might give them a push or a pull. Some things need lots of pushing and others need to be pulled along all the time.

Do you push or pull these things to make them move?

A. **hoop**   push/**pull**

B. **scooter**   push/**pull**

C. **toy**   push/**pull**

D. **yo-yo**   push/**pull**

E. **lawn mower**   push/**pull**

F. **push chair**   push/**pull**

G. **cart**   push/**pull**

H. **roller**   push/**pull**

Everyday we use up more oil, coal and gas to make electricity. Because of this, scientists are looking at ways of using wind, water and the sun to produce electricity. More and more people around the world are now using electricity produced like this.

Look at these pictures. They show some ways of producing electricity.

1

Lots of windmills together are called a wind farm.
Colour the arms of the windmill.

2

These panels use the sun's rays to produce electricity.
Colour the panels.

3

The fast-moving water from the waterfall can be used to help make electricity.
Colour the waterfall.

Levers are very useful to us. They can lift things that we cannot, such as a heavy stone or box. They can be used to open a tin or turn something. Levers work like a seesaw. Someone pushes down one end and the other person goes up. A wheelbarrow, a screwdriver and a bottle opener are all types of levers.

Look at these levers. What can they be used for?

1

a screwdriver can be used to

_____

4

scissors can be used to

_____

2

a nutcracker can be used to

_____

5

a wheelbarrow can be used to

_____

3

a pair of pliers can be used to

_____

6

garden shears can be used to

_____

Some levers work on their own. Others work in pairs. Levers that work on their own include a screwdriver and a bottle opener. Levers that work in pairs include garden shears and nutcrackers. Levers make life a lot easier because they do a lot of the work.

Look at these levers. Put an 'O' by those that work on their own. Put a 'P' by those that work in pairs.

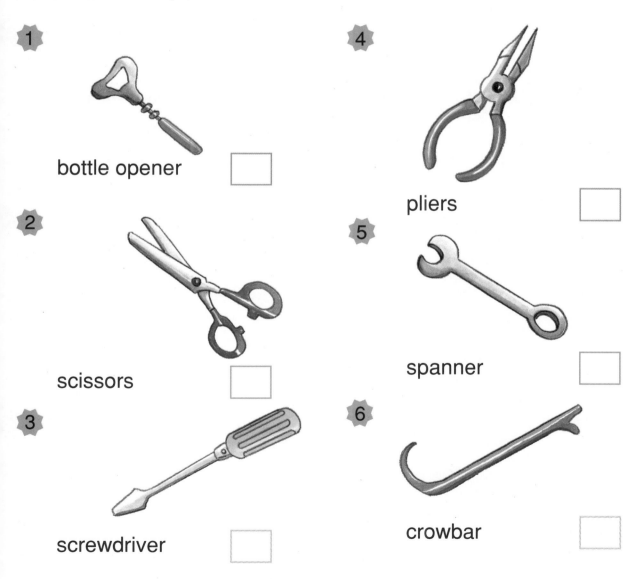

1   bottle opener ☐

2   scissors ☐

3   screwdriver ☐

4   pliers ☐

5   spanner ☐

6   crowbar ☐

ANSWERS

Chapter 1. paper clip, metal spoon.

Chapter 2. 1. The number of pins the magnet picks up will depend on how strong the magnet is; 2. It may be weaker if you only stroke it 40 times; 3. They will attract or repel.

Chapter 3. A2, B1, C4, D3.

Chapter 4. attract; repel.

Chapter 6. 1. North, 2. attract, 3. clip, 4. repel, 5. push, 6. needle.

Chapter 7. 1. South, 2. East, 3. North West, 4. South East, 5. West, 6. North East.

Chapter 13. A. chemical paste, B. carbon rod, C. case; 1. battery, 2 dangerous, 3. torches, 4. run, 5 weaker.

Chapter 14. 1. yes, 2. no, 3. yes, 4. no, 5. no.

Chapter 15. C and F.

Chapter 17. N1, 4, 5, 7; M 2, 3, 6, 8.

Chapter 19. Tick 1, 3, 7; Cross 2, 4, 5, 6,8.

Chapter 23. A. Hello B. Good Day. C. Pretty Polly. D. Help. E. Welcome. F. Stop.

Chapter 24. B.

Chapter 25. 1. wind, 2. wind, 3. engine, 4. water, 5. pedals, 6. wind; A, B, D.

Chapter 26. A. push, B. push, C. pull, D. push, E. push, F. push, G. pull, H. push.

Chapter 28. 1. tighten and undo screws, 2. crack nuts, 3. cut wire, 4. cut paper, 5. transport loads from one place to another, 6. cut grass, twigs.

Chapter 29. 1. O, 2. P, 3. O, 4. P, 5. O, 6. O.